MARVEL HEROES

KT-546-871

INSIDE ›

MARVEL

© 2015 MARVEL

FSC
www.fsc.org
MIX
Paper from
responsible sources
FSC® C005461

£7.99

Marvel Heroes Annual 2016 is published by Panini Publishing, a division of Panini UK Limited. Office of publication: Panini UK Ltd. Brockbourne House, 77 Mount Ephraim, Tunbridge Wells, Kent, TN4 8BS. MARVEL, AVENGERS and all related characters: TM & © 2015 Marvel Entertainment, LLC and its subsidiaries. Licensed by Marvel Characters B.V. www.marvel.com. All rights reserved. No similarity between any of the names, characters, persons and/or institutions in this edition with those of any living or dead person or institution is intended, and any such similarity which may exist is purely coincidental. This publication may not be sold, except by authorised dealers, and is sold subject to the condition that it shall not be sold or distributed with any part of its cover or markings removed, nor in a mutilated condition. This publication is produced under licence from Marvel Characters, Inc. through Panini S.p.A. Printed in Italy. ISBN: 978-1-84653-215-3

CAPTAIN AMERICA

ORIGIN

Ever since the dark days of World War Two, Captain America has courageously fought to protect the world from danger. Read on to find out all about him!

With his physical abilities **boosted** by a secret experimental serum, Steve Rogers was the U.S.A.'s secret weapon during World War Two. As Captain America, he undertook many dangerous missions to help the allied forces defeat the **Nazis**.

Tragedy struck in 1945 when Cap was seemingly killed whilst trying to defuse an **experimental drone missile** created by the evil Baron Zemo. The missile exploded over the North Atlantic Ocean, sending Cap's body plunging into the **icy depths** below.

Cap's indestructible shield is made from an alloy of vibranium and steel.

Years later his body was found **entombed** in a block of ice. Somehow the experimental serum had kept him in a state of **perfect hibernation.**

Once thawed out, Cap found himself in a world **unrecognizable** to the one he'd known in the past. However, he still stood by his duty to **uphold freedom and liberty,** and now protects a **whole new generation** from Super Villain threats.

DID YOU KNOW?

During **World War Two,** Cap had a teenage sidekick called Bucky. Though Bucky was thought killed on Cap's final mission, he re-surfaced years later as the Winter Soldier!

STAT BOX:

REAL NAME:
Steve Rogers

HEIGHT:
188 CM

WEIGHT:
99.8 Kg

EYES:
Blue

HAIR:
Blond

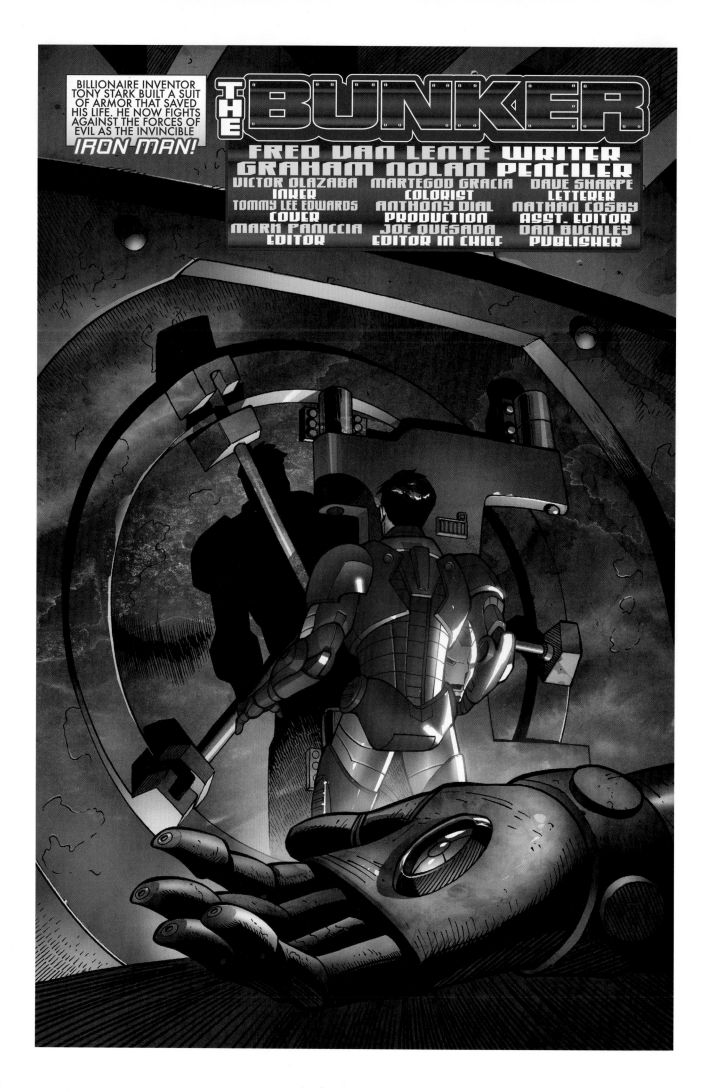

BILLIONAIRE INVENTOR TONY STARK BUILT A SUIT OF ARMOR THAT SAVED HIS LIFE. HE NOW FIGHTS AGAINST THE FORCES OF EVIL AS THE INVINCIBLE *IRON MAN!*

THE BUNKER

FRED VAN LENTE WRITER
GRAHAM NOLAN PENCILER

VICTOR OLAZABA
INKER

MARTEGOD GRACIA
COLORIST

DAVE SHARPE
LETTERER

TOMMY LEE EDWARDS
COVER

ANTHONY DIAL
PRODUCTION

NATHAN COSBY
ASST. EDITOR

MARK PANICCIA
EDITOR

JOE QUESADA
EDITOR IN CHIEF

DAN BUCKLEY
PUBLISHER

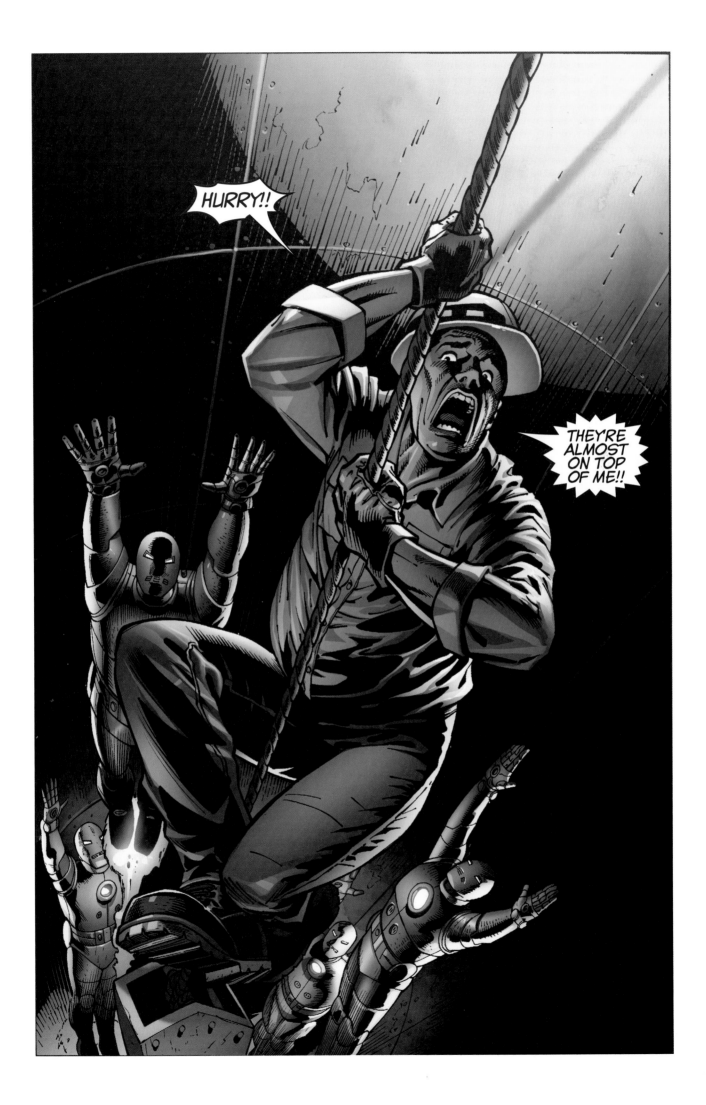

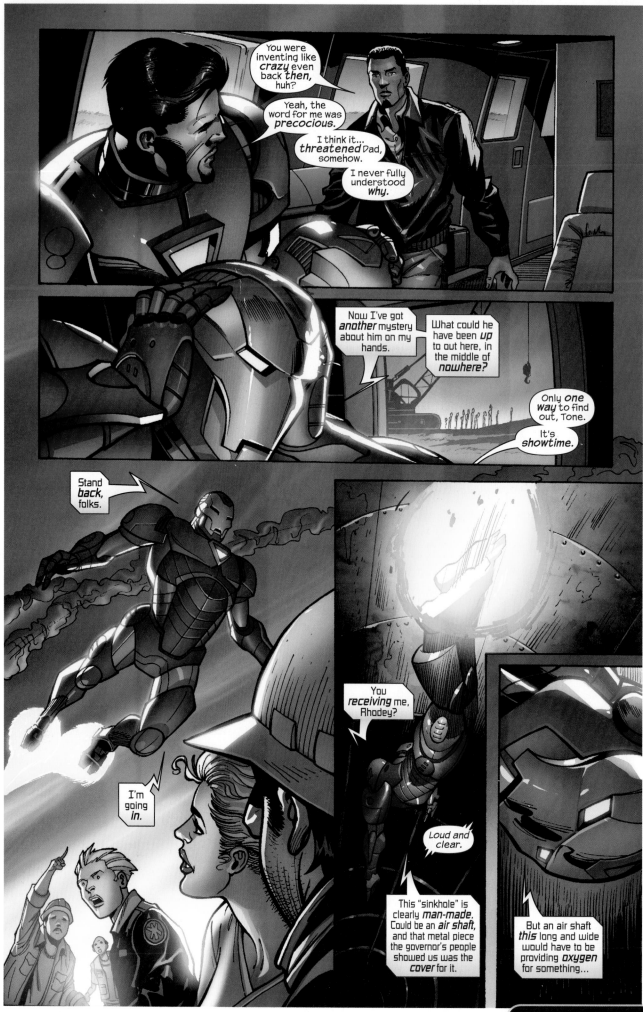

CONTINUED ON P18

CAPTAIN AMERICA'S A-MAZE-ING SHIELD

Captain America has many heroic traits, but his refusal to give up in the face of a challenge is legendary. Test your own determination by finding a path through EVERY ONE of the shields in the maze below!

START

FINISH FINISH FINISH FINISH FINISH

IRON MAN

ORIGIN

Wounded and captured by enemies, billionaire inventor Anthony Stark used his ingenuity to create a suit of high-tech armour which he utilized to escape. Now Stark uses the armour to fight evil as the invincible Iron Man.

Iron Man has many mission-specific suits, including Space Armour, Deep Sea Armour and even Hulkbuster Armour!

DATA BOX:

REAL NAME:
Anthony "Tony" Stark

HEIGHT:
186 cm
198 cm (in armour)

WEIGHT:
102 kg
193 kg (in armour)

EYES:
Blue

HAIR:
Black

ABILITIES

Iron Man's armour is an incredible piece of technology. It flies, protects the wearer from harm, and fires repulsor rays. The armour has a powerful onboard computer and a built-in air supply.

THOR

DATA BOX:

REAL NAME:
Thor Odinson

HEIGHT:
198 cm

WEIGHT:
290 kgs

EYES:
Blue

HAIR:
Blond

ORIGIN

Son of Odin, the All-Father of the realm of Asgard, Thor was a born warrior! Thor's prowess in battle led to an overabundance of pride, which Odin sought to cure by sending Thor to live on Earth as Donald Blake, a disabled human doctor.

As Donald Blake, Thor learned the value of compassion and caring, which led to Odin granting Thor the use of both identities.

POWERS

Thor possesses superhuman strength, durability and endurance and he is an exceptionally skilled warrior. Thor wields Mjolnir, a hammer forged from uru metal. Mjolnir is a superb offensive and defensive weapon that also empowers Thor to fly, open dimensional portals and command the elements of the storm.

OPERATION:

ATTEN-SHUN! General Ross here. Even though Bruce Banner is in control of the Hulk we still need to make sure he's at his absolute peak to take on the next alien menace.

Help us put Banner through his paces by completing these missions!

TRAINING AREA 01

Bruce Banner might be a genius, but can he keep it together in the heat of battle? Help him prove he's got the right stuff by working out which route the Hulk needs to take in order to avoid the Hulkbusters?

START!

FINISH!

EYE SPY!

Even though Banner normally wears glasses, it seems that the Hulk has perfect eyesight. Can you help us check his vision by spotting which of the Hulk's enemies are lurking in the shadows?

A.

B.

C.

D.

1. ABOMINATION   2. M.O.D.O.K.   3. THE LEADER   4. THE RHINO

GAMMA GUARDIAN

ULTIMATE FIGHTER!

Banner needs to make sure he uses his most effective moves when helping the Avengers. Add up the numbers next to each attack to work out which is the strongest.

SUPER PUNCH!

$5 + 4 + 2 =$

EARTHQUAKE POUND!

$3 + 2 + 2 =$

GAMMA SLAM!

$5 + 3 + 2 =$

THUNDER CLAP!

$5 + 3 + 1 =$

THE STRONGEST ATTACK IS

....

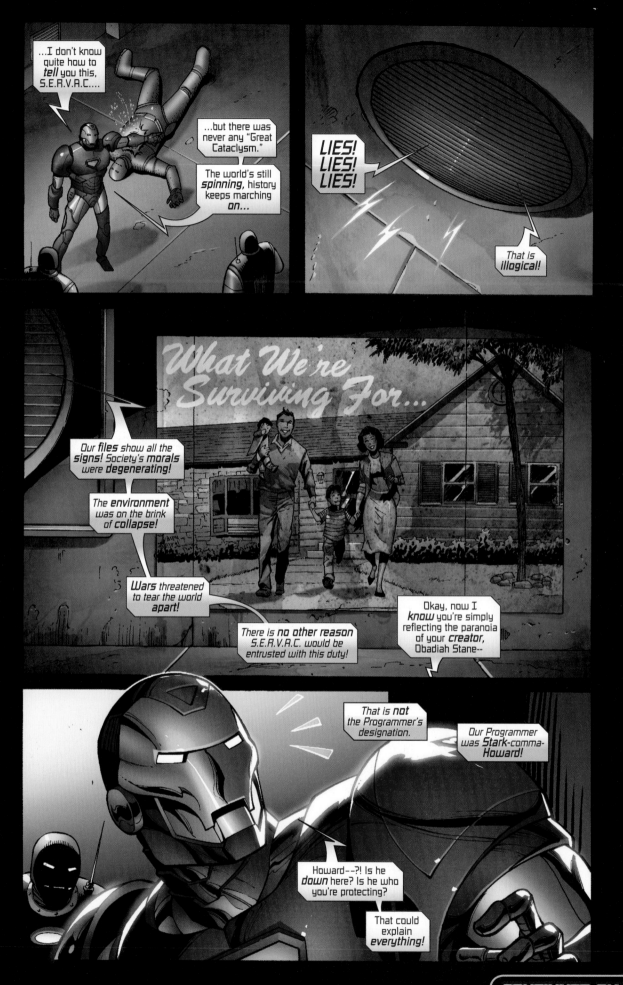

CONTINUED ON P26

24

THE INCREDIBLE HULK

DATA BOX:

REAL NAME:
Robert Bruce Banner

HEIGHT:
177 Cm. (Banner);
210 Cm. (Hulk)

WEIGHT:
58 Kgs. (Banner);
472 - 635 Kgs. (Hulk)

EYES:
Brown (Banner);
Green (Hulk)

HAIR:
Brown (Banner);
Green (Hulk)

ORIGIN

Brilliant scientist Bruce Banner was accidentally bombarded by a massive blast of gamma radiation. Now, in times of stress, Banner is cursed to transform into the living engine of destruction known as the incredible Hulk.

POWERS

The Hulk possesses extraordinary superhuman physical abilities. He is incredibly durable and can leap hundreds of miles at a time. Most importantly, the angrier the Hulk gets, the stronger he gets!

TWENTY YEARS AGO:

"Everything I've ever *wondered* about since the day I came home from my freshman year at *M.I.T.*"

Jarvis! What's *happened*? Why are there so many *reporters* out front?

I-I'd best let your *mother* explain, young master Anthony...

Mom!

What's *wrong*?

Your father has *abandoned* us, Tony! He cleaned out the contents of our family's *safe-deposit boxes* and *disappeared*!

And the *accountants* tell me our company *finances* are a *disaster*! We're on the brink of *bankruptcy*! I don't know what we'll *do*!

Don't *cry*, Mom--I'll leave *school*--I'll turn the company around...

...somehow...

"And I *did* turn it around, thanks to my *inventions*."

"But not without *two years* of *sleepless nights* for Mom and me."

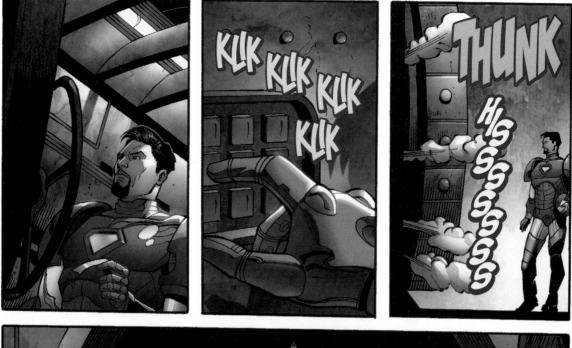

KLIK KLIK KLIK KLIK

THUNK

HISSSSSSSS

RRAAAATTTLE

Hello.

My name is HOWARD STARK.

I have no idea WHO or even WHEN anybody will be WATCHING this.

33

SPY GAMES!

HIGH-SEAS HIJACK!

Greetings, Comrades. According to my intel, the hijackers fled the ship in a helicopter. Luckily, S.H.I.E.L.D.'s satellites have tracked the chopper's flight path. Can you work out its current location by following the co-ordinates below?

5 squares east
3 squares south
4 squares west
2 squares south
3 squares east
1 square north
2 squares east

START

THE BLACK WIDOW!

As deadly as she is beautiful, Natasha Romanov AKA the Black Widow is S.H.I.E.L.D.'S most highly decorated espionage agent.

A B C D E F G

1 2 3 4 5 6 7 8

N W E S

ISLAND INFILTRATION!

START

Excellent work! The hijackers have set up camp on this small island. I need to break into the main compound without alerting anyone. See if you can find a safe route through the jungle, whilst avoiding all the guards.

FINISH!

Listen up, Heroes. Armed mercenaries have hijacked a cargo ship transporting experimental weapons from Stark Industries. S.H.I.E.L.D.'s top super spy, the Black Widow is on the case, so help her out by completing these missions.

CODE CRACKER!

Oh, no! It looks like the weapons have already left the island. I've managed to steal one of the guard's datapads, but all the information is encrypted. Help me find out where the weapons have gone by decoding this transmission!

A	B	C	D	E	F	G	H	I	J

K	L	M	N	O	P	Q	R	S

T	U	V	W	X	Y	Z

THE SHIPMENT WILL BE DELIVERED TO:

ESCAPE ROUTE!

1.

2.

3.

4.

Okay, we have the location - now all I need to do is get off the island. S.H.I.E.L.D. have sent a jet to pick me up, but there's a whole load of guards between me and it. Can you scout ahead and find out which path will lead me to the jet?

HAMMER TIME!

Help Thor defeat the evil Hela and her army of undead warriors by spotting the TEN differences between these two pictures!

YOU WON'T ESCAPE MY CLUTCHES THIS TIME, ODIN-SPAWN!

I SAY THEE NAY, WITCH! ALL THOSE WHO FOLLOW THE PATH OF EVIL SHALL FALL BENEATH THE POWER OF MJOLNIR!

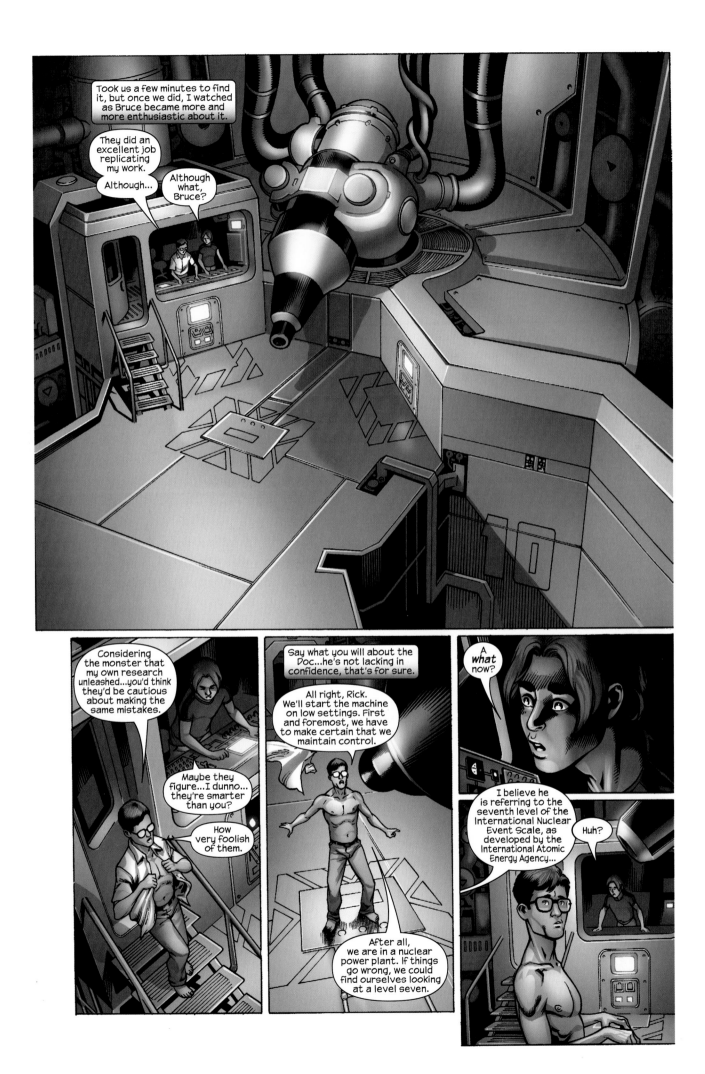

CONTINUED ON P46

ARMOUR

Greetings, guys - Tony Stark here. I'm just testing out my latest upgrades to the Iron Man armour and I could do with your help. lend me a hand by solving these challenges!

First up, we need to see how much the new quantum-servos in the arms and legs have improved the suit's strength.

HEAVY METAL!

Find out by adding up the weight of all these things I've been able to lift.

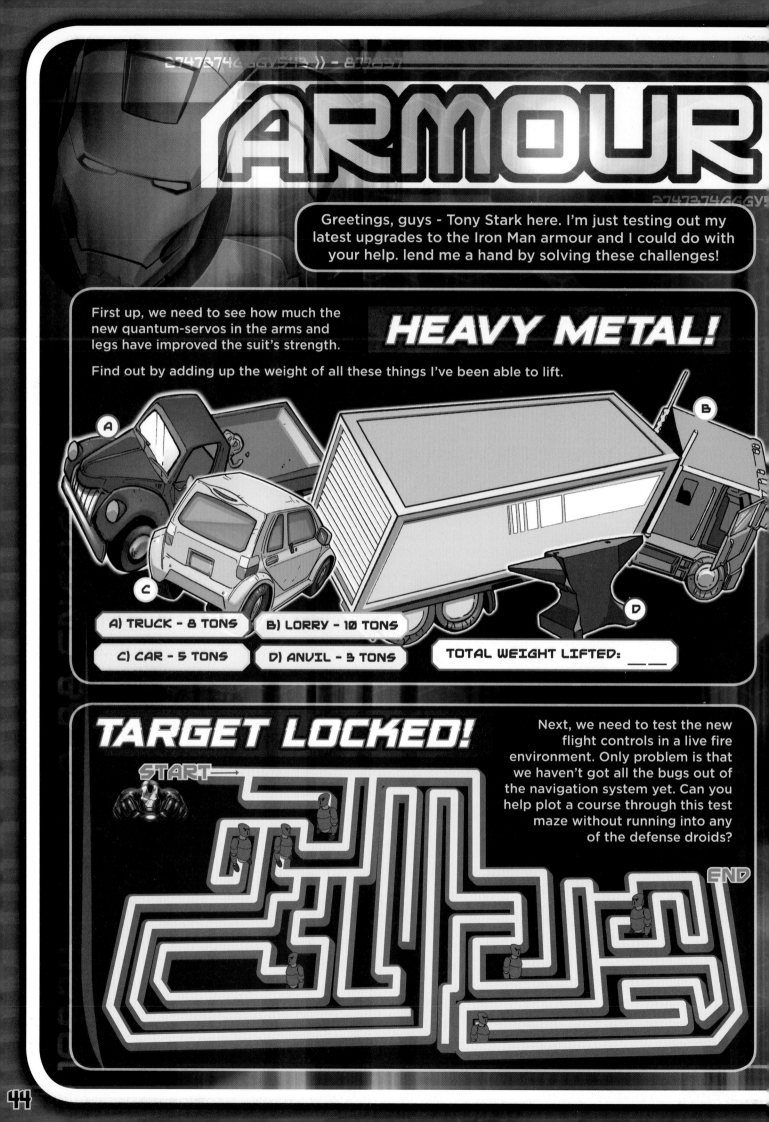

A) TRUCK - 8 TONS

B) LORRY - 10 TONS

C) CAR - 5 TONS

D) ANVIL - 3 TONS

TOTAL WEIGHT LIFTED: ___

TARGET LOCKED!

START →

END

Next, we need to test the new flight controls in a live fire environment. Only problem is that we haven't got all the bugs out of the navigation system yet. Can you help plot a course through this test maze without running into any of the defense droids?

UPGRADE!

877837

O	T	Y	I	B	C	X	A	R	A
M	A	N	D	A	R	I	N	R	L
E	B	S	Q	L	O	V	X	E	Y
Z	A	M	F	P	S	X	D	G	A
N	G	Y	A	Z	S	B	K	N	S
O	H	B	Z	U	B	R	A	O	A
R	O	X	P	K	O	D	O	M	P
A	S	N	Q	N	N	R	V	N	M
B	T	A	J	H	E	G	A	O	X
A	L	Y	M	A	S	B	P	R	A
O	M	A	G	N	E	T	O	I	S

DATA BLAST!

Hmmm... It seems that all the data in the suit's Super Villain database has been scrambled. Help us get it back in order by spotting all the names hidden in this word grid.

GHOST   MAGNETO

IRON MONGER

CROSSBONES

MANDARIN MODOK

BARON ZEMO

ARMY OF IRON!

The new suit features a holo-projection unit that can create 4 hard light copies of the Iron Man armour. See if you can work out which of these is the real thing by spotting which one matches the original blueprint exactly.

A.

B.

C.

D.

E.

ORIGINAL:

CONTINUED FROM P43

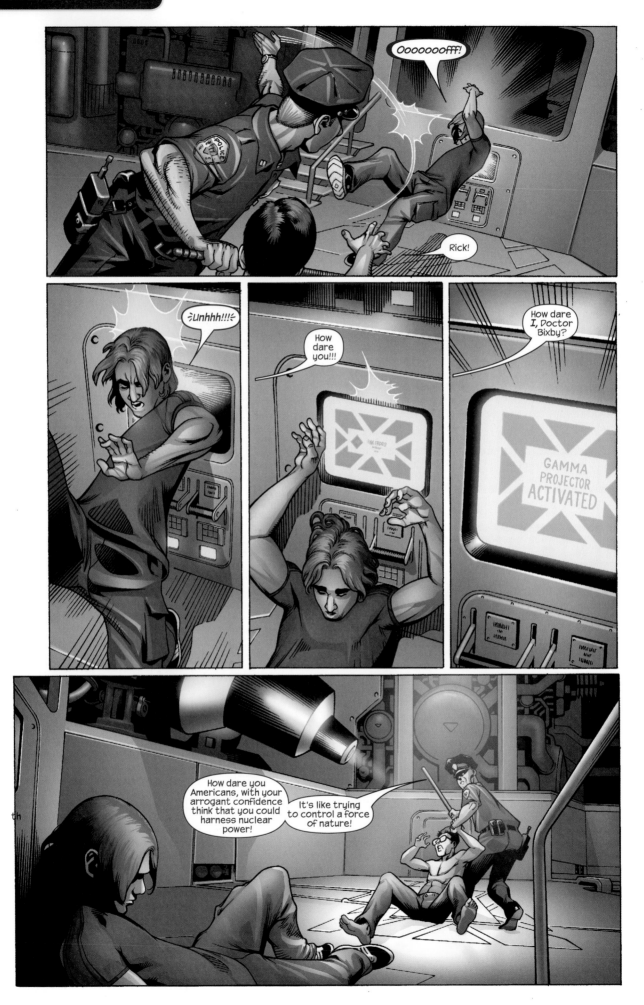

55

WHO WOULD WIN?

INSTRUCTIONS

Hulk vs. Thor — who will win in a battle between the amazing Asgardian Warrior and the Incredible Hulk? Read each category below, and make a check next to who you think would win. When you're done, add up the checks — whoever has the most is the winner! Write the winner's name in the space below.

TRAINING

THOR: Thor has been trained for war since childhood. He excells in swordsmanship and hand to hand combat!
HULK: As if ol' greenskin needs training! He's as powerful as they come!

STRENGTH

THOR: The son of Odin's strength and endurance are almost greater than anyone's!
HULK: The jade giant has incredible superhuman strength and the madder he gets, the stronger he gets!

WEAPONS

THOR: The mighty hammer 'Mjolnir' strikes fear in his enemies!
HULK: His mighty fists are all he needs!

SPEED

THOR: He is far faster than any normal human; in fact, he can move faster than the human eye can see.
HULK: His incredible strength enables him to jump across great distances. The Hulk has been known to cover hundreds of miles in a single mighty leap.

MAGIC

THOR: With his magic hammer Mjolnir, Thor has great powers, as well as the Odinforce, which enables him to tap into the near-infinite resources of cosmic and mystical energies, enhancing all of his abilities.
HULK: With his magic...uh...his magic...well, let's face it, when you're as strong as the Hulk, do you really need magic?

IT'S YOUR CALL!

WINNER:

ANSWERS

13 A-MAZE-ING SHIELD

START

FINISH FINISH FINISH FINISH FINISH

16 OPERATION GAMMA GUARDIAN

START

FINISH

SUPER PUNCH!
5 + 4 + 2 = 11

EARTHQUAKE POUND!
3 + 2 + 2 = 7

GAMMA SLAM!
5 + 3 + 2 = 10

THUNDER CLAP!
5 + 3 + 1 = 9

THE STRONGEST ATTACK IS
Super Punch

A. The Leader, B. The Rhino
C. M.O.D.O.K, D. Abomination

34 SPY GAMES

A B C D E F G
1 2 3 4 5 6 7 8

X

THE SHIPMENT WILL BE DELIVERED TO:
SAN ALVADOR

START FINISH!

1.
2.
3.
4.

36 HAMMER TIME

44 ARMOUR UPGRADE

TOTAL WEIGHT LIFTED: 26

Army of Iron - D is
the real armour

START END